Avoiding danger from underground services

London: TSO

Published by TSO (The Stationery Office), part of Williams Lea, and available from:

Online
www.tsoshop.co.uk

Mail, Telephone & E-mail
TSO
PO Box 29, Norwich, NR3 1GN
Telephone orders/General enquiries: 0333 202 5070
E-mail: customer.services@tso.co.uk
Textphone: 0333 202 5077

First published 1989
Third edition 2014

ISBN 978 0 7176 6584 6

Printed in the United Kingdom for The Stationery Office.
SD000100 10/23

This guidance is issued by the Health and Safety Executive. Following the guidance is not compulsory, unless specifically stated, and you are free to take other action. But if you do follow the guidance you will normally be doing enough to comply with the law. Health and safety inspectors seek to secure compliance with the law and may refer to this guidance.

Acknowledgments

Figure 3 is reproduced with permission of Electricity North West and PelicanCorp.
Figure 4 is reproduced with permission of National Grid.

Contents

Introduction *1*

Who is this guidance for? *1*
Where does the guidance apply? *1*
How to use the guidance *1*
Terms used in the guidance *1*

Identifying and managing the dangers *2*

Underground services: the dangers *2*
    Electricity cables *2*
    Gas pipes *2*
    Water pipes and sewers *2*
    Other pipelines *2*
    Telecommunication cables *3*
Working safely *3*

Planning the work *5*

Obtaining information on services *5*
    Electricity *5*
    Gas *5*
    Other services *5*
    Provision of plans by service owners *5*
Use and limitation of plans *8*
    Service identification surveys *8*
Your duties as a client *8*
Your duties as a designer *8*
    New housing developments (example) *9*
    Major hazard pipelines (example) *10*
    Installing new services near existing services *10*
Your duties as a contractor *10*
    Emergency work *11*

Detecting, identifying and marking underground services *12*

Detecting services *12*
Types of detecting devices or locators *13*
Using a detecting device *14*

Safe excavation *15*

Exposing services *15*
Protective clothing *17*
Identifying exposed services *17*
Marking identified services *18*
Safety at excavations *18*
Backfilling *18*
    Use of concrete as backfill *18*
Updating plans *18*
Electricity cables *18*
Cables in concrete *19*
Gas pipelines *19*
    Gas leak or damage *20*
    Other work near gas pipelines *20*
Water pipes and sewers *20*
Major hazard pipelines *20*
Permit to work *21*
Some specific sites and situations *21*
    Safe systems of work for trenchless methods *21*
    Demolition sites *22*

Appendix 1: Legislation *23*

References and further reading *26*

Further information *29*

Introduction

1   This guidance outlines the potential dangers of working near underground services and gives advice on how to reduce the risks. It deals principally with risks to health and safety rather than damage to services. However, precautions taken which reduce risks to people's health and safety will generally also reduce the risk of damage to services, which can directly or indirectly pose a risk to people's health and safety.

Who is this guidance for?

2   The guidance is aimed at all of those involved in commissioning, planning, managing and carrying out work on or near underground services, as well as the owners and operators of such services.

Where does the guidance apply?

3   The guidance applies to situations where underground services may be found and disturbed, including:

- street works;
- road works;
- excavation, drilling and piling;
- demolition and site remediation;
- site investigation surveys;
- any other work that involves penetrating the ground at or below surface level.

Underground services are widespread. Assume they are present unless you have been shown otherwise.

How to use the guidance

4   The guidance is divided into four chapters:

- Identifying and managing the dangers;
- Planning the work;
- Detecting, identifying and marking underground services;
- Safe excavation.

Guidance on the general precautions to prevent damage to all types of underground services is in the sections 'Planning the work' and 'Detecting, identifying and marking underground services'. Additional guidance for particular services is in the 'Safe excavation' section.

Terms used in the guidance

Service(s)
5   All underground pipes, cables and equipment associated with electricity, gas, water (including piped sewage) and telecommunications. Also includes other pipelines which transport a range of petrochemical and other fluids. It does not include underground structures such as railway tunnels etc.

Service connection(s)
6   Pipes or cables between distribution mains and individual premises.

Emergency work
7   Work that needs to be done immediately to repair damaged services in order to prevent continuing risk(s) to health and safety either directly, such as stopping a gas leak, or indirectly when restoring power to traffic signals at a major junction. It does not mean restoration of service to meet customer service targets.

Client
8   Any person or organisation for whom a project or work is carried out.

Design
9   Includes drawings, design details, specifications and bills of quantities. A designer is anyone who prepares or modifies these; for example, people planning the route of a new cable television scheme are designers.

Identifying and managing the dangers

Underground services: the dangers

10 Damage to underground services can cause fatal or severe injury as well as significant disruption and environmental damage; it can also delay the project and incur considerable costs.

Case study 1

A construction company paid £210 000 in fines and costs after an employee died in an explosion following damage to an 11 000-volt live cable within an excavation.

The worker suffered burns over 60% of his body while he and other workers were using breakers and a shovel within the excavation. He died of his injuries 13 days later. The company had not informed workers that there were live cables in the excavation and failed to put adequate measures in place to prevent them being damaged.

Electricity cables

11 Injuries are usually caused by the explosive effects of arcing current, and by any associated fire or flames that may result when a live cable is penetrated by a sharp object such as the point of a tool (see front cover). Such effects can also occur when a cable is crushed severely enough to cause internal contact between the conductors, or between metallic sheathing and one or more conductors. Typically, injuries are severe – potentially fatal – burns to the hands, face and body; electric shock is possible but less likely.

12 Incidents may also arise from cables, connections and terminations which have been damaged but left unreported and unrepaired, or which have deteriorated with age.

13 Other nearby services, such as plastic gas pipes, may also be at risk from damaged live electricity cables. This could result in explosions and a greater fire risk.

Gas pipes

14 Damage to gas pipes and connections can cause leaks that may lead to fire or explosion. There are two types of damage:

- damage that causes an immediate leak;
- damage that causes a leak some time later.

The damage may occur when the work is carried out, or subsequently; for example, poor reinstatement may leave a pipe inadequately supported or subject to unequal forces.

15 The risk from leaking liquified petroleum gas (LPG) is greater than from a natural gas leak as it is heavier than air and does not disperse so readily. It can also travel great distances below ground level before accumulating at low level, for example in basements and cellars.

Water pipes and sewers

16 Although damage to water pipes is less likely to result in injury, the following may occur:

- A jet of water from a main can be of sufficient pressure and intensity to injure a person. It may also contain stones or other hard objects ejected from the ground around the pipe.
- Leaks of water from underground pipes can affect adjacent services and reduce support for other structures.
- Damage to mains pipes can result in flooding, leading to subsequent risks from drowning or the rapid collapse of support to the sides of an excavation; water can enter gas pipes if they are also damaged.

17 While some sewage is pumped at pressure, sewers are generally gravity-fed and the main risks from damage to a sewer are to the health of workers from exposure to raw sewage, the chance of ground collapse and possibility of environmental contamination and pollution.

Other pipelines

18 The danger arising from damage to other pipelines depends on the nature of the conveyed fluid. Fluids and their associated risks include:

Figure 1 Aftermath of a gas explosion, following damage to an underground gas service pipe

- flammable liquids and gases – risk of fire and explosion;
- fluids at elevated pressure – risk of injury from sudden release of contents;
- toxic liquids and gases – risk of poisoning;
- inert gases such as nitrogen and argon – risk of asphyxiation.

19 Very often a fluid will present a combination of risks; for example, a liquid may be both toxic and flammable.

Telecommunication cables
20 Damage to telecommunication and TV cables may require expensive repairs and can cause considerable disruption to those relying on the system. However, the risk of personal injury to workers is normally very low.

21 Flammable and toxic gases can enter cable-carrying ducts, particularly if the duct has been damaged. Such gases can accumulate in chambers,

manholes etc and pose a risk to operatives who may need to work there.

Working safely

22 A safe system of work has three basic elements:

- planning the work;
- detecting, identifying and marking underground services;
- safe excavation/safe digging practices.

23 These key elements complement each other, and all three are essential when working near underground services. More details of each are given in the chapters that follow. A flow diagram, outlining the process, is at Figure 2.

24 Anyone planning or undertaking work that may disturb underground services must contact the owners/operators of those services for information

about the location and status of the services. Those owners and operators should in turn provide any relevant information about the location of services in the work area. Service owners and operators should be prepared to help locate and identify the services (for example, by sending a representative to the site). Long-term plans or formal arrangements for co-operation may be needed with other utilities, local authorities and contractors who carry out road and footway excavation.

25 Plan work to avoid underground services. Where this is not possible, develop plans to minimise the risk of damage to those services in the work area.

26 Detecting underground services will require information from those who own the services. Individuals with sufficient experience and technical knowledge should carry out a comprehensive survey of the work area using the appropriate survey tools and equipment.

27 When carrying out excavations, it is important that:

- those supervising and carrying out the work have sufficient skills, knowledge and experience to do so safely;
- safe working practices are put in place and used;
- appropriate traffic signing is used on highways; this is described in *Safety at street works and road works. A Code of Practice*[1] and chapter 8 of the *Traffic signs manual;*[2,3]
- risks from other sources, such as collapse of excavations, are avoided;
- adequate welfare facilities are available to those doing the work.

A brief look at the process from referring to plans on site to the start of work near underground services

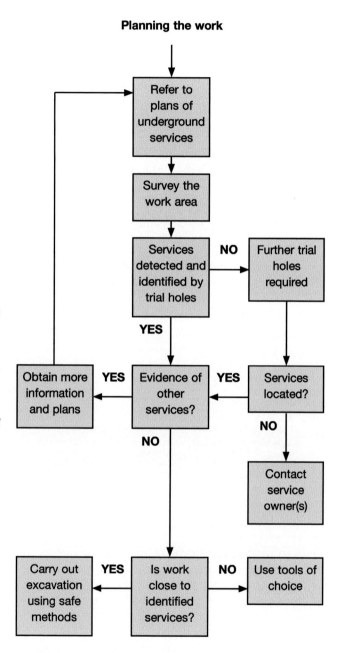

Figure 2 A safe system of work

Planning the work

In summary

Identify clearly the extent of the work area and find out what underground services are within the area before considering whether they are likely to be disturbed:

- Obtain service drawings from utilities companies and other organisations with relevant information about the site.
- Survey the site to identify the services and other underground structures. Record the location of any services.
- Review/assess the planned work to avoid disturbing services where possible.
- Allow sufficient time and provide sufficient resource to do the work safely.
- Emergency work still requires planning and assessment of the risks arising from the work. A precautionary approach must be taken when breaking ground.

Obtaining information on services

28 Obtain plans or other suitable information about all underground services in the area when the work is being planned. Wherever possible, you must consult owners/operators. Remember that for some services there may be more than one owner/operator.

29 There are a number of 'one-call' services available that can simplify the process of identifying who may have underground services in the work area and arranging for copies of plans and service records to be provided. Some of these services are free to use while others may charge.

30 Where it is not possible for those undertaking the work to obtain information, as may be the case when emergency work has to be undertaken, the work **must** be carried out as though there are underground services in the area.

Electricity
31 Most electrical service cables belong to the

regional distribution network operator (DNO). However, some cables belong to other bodies, such as: the highway or roads authority; the street lighting authority; electricity generating companies; National Grid; Ministry of Defence; railway operator (usually Network Rail); Independent Distribution Network Operators (IDNOs); or other companies.

Gas
32 Most underground gas pipes are operated by public gas transporters (PGTs). The main exceptions are new developments, often supplied by independent gas transporters (IGTs) and properties fed from bulk-stored LPG, where the pipes may be owned by the property owners or other private individuals. In the latter case, owners/managers should be able to provide information but on certain estates owners and managers may not be available round the clock. You can obtain further information from the LPG supplier, whose name and telephone number (manned 24 hours) should be displayed at the bulk storage vessel compound or, for underground LPG tanks, at the segregated area above the tanks.

33 Where the presence of gas pipes which operate at pressures of 2 bar (30 psig) and above is indicated, consult the owner/operator before work begins.

Other services
34 Other underground pipes may be found on or around: hospitals; airports; Ministry of Defence sites; universities; research parks; petrochemical, nuclear and other industrial sites. Where work is planned on such sites, make contact with the owner/occupier of the sites to request specific information about underground services.

35 Because of the difficulty in detecting some telecommunication cables and the cost of damage to them, telecommunication companies may prefer to visit the site to locate the cables.

Provision of plans by service owners
36 Owners should provide either up-to-date, readable plans, which show the recorded line and depth (where known) of all their known services buried in the

proposed work area, or other suitable information which achieves the same aim. A symbol key is important to help the recipient understand the plans.

37 Owners should do everything reasonably practicable to make sure that such information is made available to enquirers. They are likely to receive many routine applications for information and should consider how best to make information available at short notice. They should also make arrangements to deal with emergencies outside office hours so that operatives can be given plans of underground services when they receive their work instructions.

38 Some owners may have reservations, for reasons of security, about supplying copies of their underground services plans for areas such as those around important civil and military establishments. In such cases, an alternative method should be used; for example, a representative could be sent to the site to provide information.

Figure 3 Example of an electricity plan

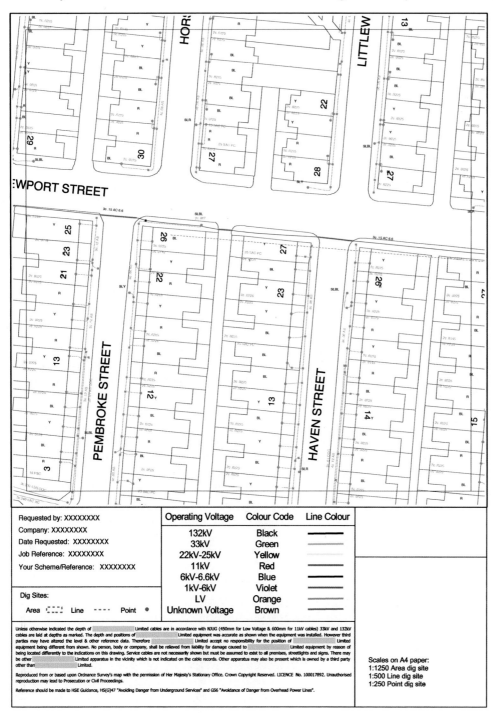

Operating Voltage	Colour Code	Line Colour
132kV	Black	——————
33kV	Green	————
22kV-25kV	Yellow	————
11kV	Red	——————
6kV-6.6kV	Blue	——————
1kV-6kV	Violet	——————
LV	Orange	——————
Unknown Voltage	Brown	——————

Requested by: XXXXXXXX
Company: XXXXXXXX
Date Requested: XXXXXXXX
Job Reference: XXXXXXXX
Your Scheme/Reference: XXXXXXXX

Dig Sites:

Area ⌐_¬ Line ---- Point ●

Unless otherwise indicated the depth of ▓▓▓▓▓▓ Limited cables are in accordance with NJUG (450mm for Low Voltage & 600mm for 11kV cables) 33kV and 132kV cables are laid at depths as marked. The depth and positions of ▓▓▓▓▓▓ Limited equipment was accurate as shown when the equipment was installed. However third parties may have altered the level and other reference data. Therefore ▓▓▓▓▓▓ Limited accept no responsibility for the position of ▓▓▓▓▓▓ Limited equipment being different from shown. No person, body or company, shall be relieved from liability for damage caused to ▓▓▓▓▓▓ Limited equipment by reason of being located differently to the indications on this drawing. Service cables are not necessarily shown but must be assumed to exist to all premises, streetlights and signs. There may be other ▓▓▓▓▓▓ Limited apparatus in the vicinity which is not indicated on the cable records. Other apparatus may also be present which is owned by a third party other than ▓▓▓▓▓▓ Limited.

Reproduced from or based upon Ordnance Survey's map with the permission of Her Majesty's Stationary Office. Crown Copyright Reserved. LICENCE No. 100017892. Unauthorised reproduction may lead to Prosecution or Civil Proceedings.

Reference should be made to HSE Guidance, HS(G)47 "Avoiding Danger from Underground Services" and GS6 "Avoidance of Danger from Overhead Power Lines".

Scales on A4 paper:
1:1250 Area dig site
1:500 Line dig site
1:250 Point dig site

Figure 4 Example of a plan of gas pipes

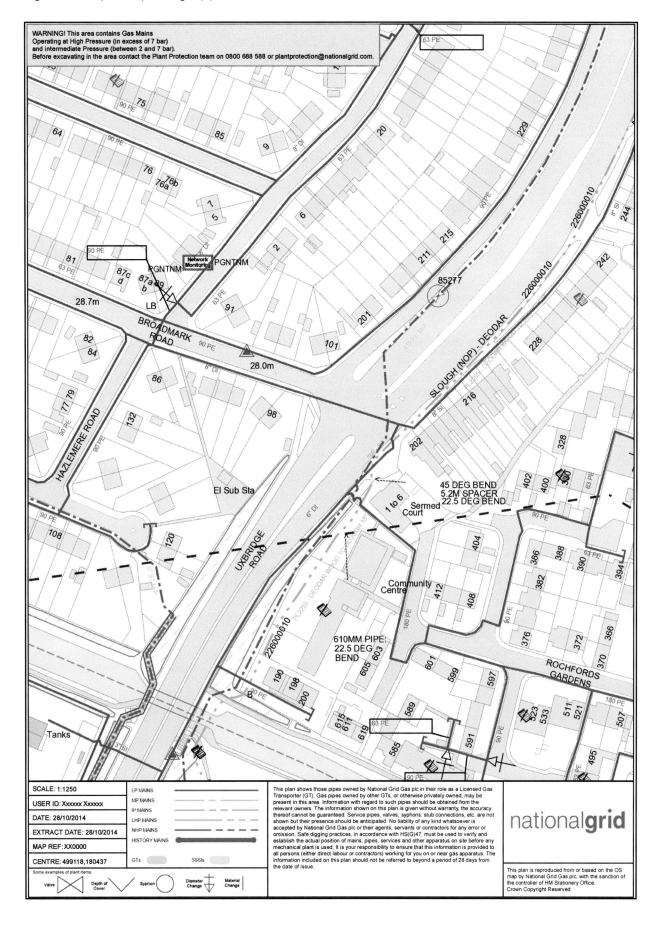

Use and limitation of plans

39 Plans alone are not sufficient to identify and locate services before starting work. They provide basic information on which to base a thorough site survey before work begins.

40 Plans vary in scale, content and style. Two examples are shown in Figures 3 and 4. Provide adequate instruction and training in how to read and interpret plans to anyone who needs to use them. Ideally, plans should be in colour to assist their interpretation and understanding.

41 Plans can give an indication of the location, configuration and number of underground services at a particular site and should help subsequent tracing by detecting devices or locators. However, they are not always drawn accurately to scale and, even if they claim to be, you should not rely on them to obtain distances or depths. For example, errors may have been made during drafting, or reproduction may have changed the scale, especially if the plan was obtained from a microfiche slide or digital map. Accuracy may be further limited because:

- the position of reference points (eg the kerb line) may have changed since the plans were drawn;
- re-grading of the surface may mean that the depths shown are now incorrect;
- services, particularly cables, may have been moved without the knowledge of their owners/operators;
- in many cases service connections are not marked;
- services marked as straight lines may, in practice, snake. Excessively long cables may have been laid in horizontal loops outside substations, switch rooms etc;
- plans may show spare ducts;
- the routes of older services in particular may not have been recorded, so the absence of records should never be taken as proof that the area in question is free of underground services.

42 These limitations make it very important that you take into account other indicators and use a suitable detecting device and safe digging methods.

43 The service location information should be copied onto the working drawings for the guidance of those carrying out the work. Information should include all relevant features, such as valve pits, depths etc. Take particular care where topographical changes have occurred since services were laid.

44 Those using or interpreting plans need to have sufficient knowledge and experience to understand what the plans show in order to determine the likely presence of services on the work site.

Case study 2

A 3-phase electrical cable was struck during excavation works by a renewable energy company. The cable was not marked with tape or tiles. The cable was shallower than shown on the plan. The work area was not surveyed to locate underground services. Relying on plans is not sufficient. The work area should be surveyed to accurately locate services shown on plans.

Service identification surveys

45 A service detection and mapping survey of the work area should be undertaken at the planning stage as its findings will be useful to the designer(s) and contractor(s) in designing out and planning to reduce the risk of damage to the underground services.

46 Time spent on a survey at this stage can save significant costs and delays to the work by allowing for the avoidance of damage to underground assets and efficient programming of the work.

47 More information on identification surveys is given in 'Detecting, identifying and marking underground services'.

Your duties as a client

48 Clients have a duty to make reasonable enquiries about underground services and pass relevant information to the designer(s) and contractor(s). Your own files and other records may contain information on underground services. If they do, remember that it may have been obtained for previous work and may be out of date. The most up-to-date information should be included in the tender information.

49 A client who is unable or unwilling to obtain this information **must** allow the contractor sufficient time and resource to do so instead.

50 Clients need to consider how contractors have addressed the risks from underground services.

Your duties as a designer

51 Designers have a duty to reduce or 'design out' the risks arising from damage to underground services. Having reduced the risks to a level as low as

reasonably practicable by design, information should be provided to those doing the work about the risks that remain. In most cases, the best way of informing contractors and individuals doing the work is by providing this on working drawings.

52 You will need to know if there are underground services present so that you can amend the design to avoid them where possible.

53 For building work, re-siting the services away from the work is often a reasonably practicable means of avoiding the risk. Ask the service owner/operator to do this and include adequate notice.

54 Other options to re-siting the services may include:

■ repositioning or redesigning structures or parts of structures to ensure that services are avoided during the work;
■ arranging for the supply to be disconnected during the work; or, if none of these are possible;
■ choosing methods to avoid the services; for example, by using ground beams to bridge or span the services.

55 For electricity cables more than other services, there may be a need to make them dead for the work to proceed safely. Contact electricity companies as early as possible to allow them to isolate supplies. Plan project schedules to allow sufficient time for this to happen.

56 If the cable cannot be made dead, an alternative safe way of doing the work will be required.

57 Permanent structures such as buildings should generally not be built over services, nor should services be encased in concrete as this may introduce additional risks to construction workers and can prevent future access to the services. If it is not possible to avoid building structures over any service, make arrangements with the utility to relocate the services in a duct or something similar.

58 Consider the location of underground gas pipelines when planning building, excavation, landfill or other such work. Such activities may either cause damage to the pipelines or deny access to them for maintenance purposes. Make suitable arrangements for future access and maintenance before undertaking the work.

59 Consider ancillary work, including the erection of perimeter fencing and walling, or the position of

temporary and permanent roadways onto the site that may affect underground services at the site perimeter. Early identification and planning are essential if you are to control risks during the entire construction phase of the project, including enabling works.

Case study 3

A self-employed sub-contractor was burnt when he struck a 415 V electrical cable with an electrical breaker he was using to break up some concrete. The client had chosen to build over the cable rather than have it diverted. The cable had been protected by a conduit and its location was known. The client did not tell the contractor of its location before starting work and the contractor did not ask. The cable was diverted following the incident.

Some specific situations

New housing developments
Underground services within the confines of partly completed housing developments are especially prone to damage from ongoing construction work. Each utility company should keep to its agreed position; see *Guidelines on the positioning of underground utilities apparatus for new development sites Volume 2.*[4] A common trench may help to control the position and separation of underground services. Special arrangements may be necessary to restrict vehicle and mobile plant crossings to locations where temporary protection for the services has been provided.

Where new services such as electrical or gas supplies are being installed, it may be possible to reduce risks by not installing or commissioning them until other groundworks and work on the installation have been completed. This should be considered early in the design process to allow the works to be sequenced accordingly.

Close liaison should be maintained between the developers, their contractors and the utilities. The builder/developer should keep a marked-up plan of the estate showing the up-to-date position of underground services (including any variations from planned routes) on site for the information of those involved in excavation and groundwork.

Major hazard pipelines

Pipelines are used to convey a wide range of fluids, including oils and other petrochemicals, ethylene, oxygen, nitrogen and similar industrial gases and a number of other chemicals.

The more hazardous of these pipelines (known as major accident hazard pipelines) are not normally found in residential areas. They are usually in rural areas and often near chemical and petrochemical installations. Cross-country pipelines are also found on agricultural land. They usually cross roads, railways and motorways etc at right angles.

It is important to consider the location of underground pipelines before carrying out building, excavation, landfill or other such work. Such activities may not only cause damage to pipelines but could also affect future access to them for maintenance purposes. Both the landowner and local authority should be contacted for further information; it is a statutory requirement for plans of pipelines to be lodged with local authorities.

Liaison with the pipeline operator is important, as information can be provided about not only the location but also the nature of the fluid being transported, any restrictions on excavations near the pipeline, the precautions to be taken during excavating and action to be taken in an emergency. Accordingly, where work is proposed near pipelines, the specific requirements of pipeline operators should be adhered to.

Installing new services near existing services
60 New underground services often have to be laid in ground which contains existing services. Where it is reasonably practicable to do so, the designer planning the new installation should aim to site it so that it is separated from all existing underground services by the distances specified in *Guidelines on the positioning and colour coding of underground utilities' apparatus Volume 1*.[5]

61 It is important to have information about existing services to help select a route for the new service that avoids them. The risk of contact with existing services can be reduced by choosing a route with a low density of underground services. For example, a cable television duct might be routed at the side of a road if there is a reduced cable density there.

62 Designers of pipelines should also be aware of the guidance in *A guide to the Pipelines Safety Regulations 1996*,[6] which advises that the parallel running of similar pipelines in the street should be avoided. Liaison with the owners of services is important as they are in a position to provide information to the designers to enable them to make such decisions.

63 Where you cannot achieve the recommended separation, there should be as great a separation as is reasonably practicable. Where the installation of a service would obstruct access to an existing service you should use all reasonably practicable means to avoid this. In particular, avoid the practice of laying multiple ducts directly above other services. This may require diversion of services or the installation of accessible shared service ducts or chambers.

64 If the utility or its contractors laying the new service have had to reduce the separation, they should inform the owner/operator whose service has been affected so that they can then amend their records for future reference.

Your duties as a contractor

65 Contractors must prepare safe systems of work for their employees by identifying the hazards they are likely to encounter during the work and making a suitable and sufficient assessment of the risks posed by those hazards. Clear information on the type, location and status of underground services and the tools, equipment and working practices they will require to avoid damaging the services is essential.

66 Make sure that those doing the work have sufficient information, clear instruction and training to work safely, and that proper management and supervision of the work ensures that it is done safely.

67 Information about the risks from underground services should be provided before arriving on site. Where services have been disconnected, this should be recorded and information about where and when the disconnection was done should be given to the contractors working in that area. Co-operate with any principal contractor to make sure any rules or agreed methods of working are adhered to.

68 Anyone who carries out work near underground gas pipes and associated equipment should observe any specific requirements made by the gas transporter, and make sure that access to the equipment is available at all times. Do not make any unauthorised repairs to gas pipes. If in doubt, seek advice from the appropriate gas transporter.

69 Where heavy plant may have to cross the line of any vulnerable service during construction work defined crossing points should be provided and used. Keep the number of crossing points to a minimum, indicate them clearly and do not allow crossings at other places along the line of the service. Where an existing road does not adequately protect the pipe, crossing points should be suitably reinforced with sleepers, steel plates or a specially constructed reinforced concrete raft, as necessary. The owner/operator of the service will advise on the type of reinforcement necessary.

70 On completion of the work, provide information on underground services, found or newly installed, to the client and the owners of other services encountered. This will allow them to update their own records on the position of their services and should be made available to others who will need to use this information for subsequent maintenance, repair and construction work.

Emergency work

71 There will be occasions where it is necessary to do emergency work to repair damaged services in order to make them safe or restore them following damage. Often this emergency work may just require a temporary fix before a permanent repair can be done, though circumstances may mean it is appropriate to make a permanent repair immediately.

72 Routine work that does not arise from a safety-critical situation, and could be planned, should not be done as emergency work.

73 Emergency work still requires planning and assessment of the risks before and while carrying it out. Attempts must be made to obtain information about underground services in the area.

74 Inevitably, there will be greater emphasis on the work on site to locate services and excavate safely. This is not an excuse for cutting corners or running unacceptable or avoidable risks. The work must be done by individuals with sufficient knowledge and experience, and be reviewed as it is undertaken.

75 Those managing emergency work must balance the risk of potential damage to underground services against the continuing risk from the emergency situation. For example, the risk of damage to cables while isolating a gas pipe to stop a leak must be weighed against the risk of fire and explosion from the continued leak. In all cases, make sure that the overall risk to safety is not increased.

Detecting, identifying and marking underground services

In summary

Locate the services identified at the planning stage survey as being in the work area.

Make sure those involved in detecting and identifying services are competent in the proper use of survey tools and detecting devices as well as reading/interpreting plans.

Once detected, identify and mark the services and confirm their status – ie whether electricity cables are live, whether gas pipes are pressurised – and then record their location.

Detecting services

76 There are different levels of survey:

- *Desktop study:* Involves requesting and considering the service drawings from the owners of underground services. This should be done for all projects that involve excavation or penetrating the ground.
- *Desktop study and site investigation:* Involves using the information from the desktop study to assist a physical inspection of the site (looking for physical signs such as inspection hatches, reinstated excavations, street lights and telecoms boxes) and a survey using detection tools.
- *Physical identification of the services:* In addition to the above, this involves taking steps to detect and identify the underground services through trial holes to verify their location, depth and identity. It may also involve passing a tracing device through a pipe or tunnel.

77 The level of survey needed will depend on the nature of the work site. Some congested urban locations will require a more detailed survey than some brown and green field sites. The decision on the necessary level of survey should be informed by an assessment of the likelihood of underground services being present, based on the information obtained for the work site. The designer should make this decision

at the planning stage in consultation with the contractor and surveyor.

78 The results of the survey should be shared with the designer and recorded in a clear, usable format on working drawings to be shared with those working on the site and, where possible, marked out on site.

79 Those doing the survey need to have sufficient knowledge and experience in the use of survey equipment and techniques. They will need to understand the limitations of the equipment, the effect of differing ground conditions on the survey results, how to survey a given area effectively, and to appreciate the limitations of plans and drawings provided by the service owners. Some training providers offer courses in service detection and mapping and an NVQ qualification in utility mapping.

80 The position of any services in or near the proposed work area should be pinpointed as accurately as possible using a detecting device in conjunction with up-to-date service plans and other information which provides a guide to the possible location of services, and help interpret the signal.

81 Take account of any indications that underground services exist, such as the presence of lamp posts, illuminated traffic signs, gas service pipes entering buildings, pit covers, pipeline marker posts, evidence of reinstated trenches etc. However, if there are no such indications, this does not mean that there are no underground services.

82 Plans do not normally show the position of gas service connections and their existence should be assumed. It may be possible to estimate the probable line of the service connection pipe from the gas meter position, or from the point of entry into the premises.

83 Gas plant may be shown by valve boxes, pits and housings. However, covers for valve boxes and pits will sometimes not show clearly whether gas is the service present; if in doubt, contact the gas transporter.

84 Anyone selecting detection tools and survey methods must understand the range of methods and tools and their limitations. In particular, they need to be aware of the potential for false readings or signals in certain techniques as they may lead to inaccurate information being included in the plan of work and, in turn, lead to a false sense of security.

Types of detecting devices or locators

Figure 5 Using a cable locator

85 The main types available can be classed as follows:

- *Hum detectors* are receiving instruments that detect the magnetic field radiated by electricity cables which have a current flowing through them. They do not respond to:
  - cables where there is little or no current flowing; for example, service connection cables to unoccupied premises or street lighting cables in the daytime;
  - direct current cables;
  - some well-balanced high-voltage cables, where these generate relatively little field (which in turn may be further screened by the cable sheathing);
  - pot-ended cables, see paragraph 89.
- *Radio frequency detectors* are receiving instruments that respond to low-frequency radio

signals, which may be picked up and re-emitted by long metallic pipes and cables. If radio frequency detection is used, other metallic objects such as abandoned pipes, cables and tram tracks may re-radiate the signal and results may vary appreciably according to locality, length of the underground cable or pipe and distance from the termination and geographical orientation.

- *Transmitter/receiver instruments*, where a small portable transmitter or signal generator can be connected to a cable or pipe, or placed very close to it so that the signal is introduced into it. The receiver, typically the same radio frequency detectors mentioned above, can then detect this signal. Usually the location of some part of the cable or pipe needs to be already known so that the transmitter can be properly positioned. A direct connection is not required but accuracy will be greatly improved if a direct connection can be made. Some signal generators can be sent along pipes. They can provide useful information in difficult situations where the techniques using hum detectors and radio frequency detectors have not been successful. **Use of signal generators will significantly increase the accuracy of the service location.**
- *Metal detectors* are conventional detectors, which will usually locate flat metal covers, joint boxes etc, but may well miss round cables or pipes.
- *Ground probing radar* is a method capable of detecting anomalies in the ground. When these anomalies can be plotted into a continuous line it may indicate a cable, duct or pipe. However, this technique alone would not determine the precise nature of the service and it should be supported by information available about the services present and also, preferably, by the use of other more conventional forms of detecting device. Knowledge of ground conditions is important. For example, false readings are most likely where there are boulders and debris in the ground or where the ground has often been disturbed. Because of equipment costs and the need for specialist training it may be cost-effective to use firms specialising in this technique.
- *Radio frequency identification (RFID)* is a system increasingly used to mark or 'tag' new services. These markers can be programmed with information about the particular service and its depth, and this information can be read by detecting devices. The accuracy of the information depends on the marker being properly attached to the service. As a developing system, RFID will often be found on new services so will not necessarily assist with older services. RFID marker systems may require specific detecting tools that may not be compatible with one another.

86 Some instruments use more than one of the technologies listed and may include a depth-measuring facility.

Using a detecting device

87 The degree of confidence with which underground services can be detected depends on a number of factors, such as:

- the training, skill, hearing and experience of the operator;
- the characteristics of the device being used;
- the calibration and reliability of the detecting device;
- the type, length and depth of the service;
- for cables, the magnitude of the current being carried;
- the effects of other nearby services;
- the nature of surface conditions, eg reinforced concrete;
- the nature of the ground conditions;
- whether or not a signal generator is being used.

88 Anyone who uses a locator should have received thorough training in its use and limitations. Always use detection devices in accordance with the manufacturer's instructions, check and calibrate regularly, and maintain in good working order.

89 Occasionally, cables are terminated in the ground by means of a seal, sometimes with external mechanical protection. These 'pot-ended' or 'bottle-ended' cables should be treated as live and should not be assumed to be abandoned or disused. They can be difficult to detect with locators even when 'live'.

Figure 6 Congested services

90 A locator may not be able to distinguish between cables or pipes running close together and may represent them as a single signal. If, for example, two are sited one above the other the lower one may not be detected. Use signal generators whenever possible as they greatly increase the accuracy of detecting and tracing an underground service.

91 Locators (with the possible exception of ground-probing radar) do not detect plastic pipes or other non-metallic services unless:

- a metallic tracer wire has been laid with the pipe. This enables a signal transmitter/receiver to be used. Plastic gas and water pipes are the non-metallic services most likely to be encountered and few have been laid with metallic tracer wires in the past, with the exception of plastic pipes on LPG-metered estates; or
- a small signal transmitter or tracing rod is inserted into and pushed along the pipe or duct. This is a sophisticated technique which may not be appropriate for many jobs; or
- RFID markers, or similar, have been affixed to or overlay the pipes.

92 **Note:** Tracer wire(s) on a service may not be continuous due to being damaged or not properly laid out, therefore the true length of a particular service may be missed.

93 If a service recorded on a plan cannot be located, seek appropriate assistance or advice from the service owner.

94 Many telecommunication and railway signalling cables cannot be located by detecting devices, unless metal components (such as a metal sheath) are connected to earth, they have been tagged with location markers, or they are laid in ducts where tracing rods can be used.

95 Services should be traced through the full extent of the work area as they may not run in straight lines. Cables will often have kinks or loops and pipes may have joints or bends that are not shown on service drawings.

96 Use trial holes to positively identify a service and its depth. Exposing a service safely in this way will allow its status to be checked and may make it easier for a tracing signal to be applied.

97 Note the line of any identified services and mark with waterproof crayon, chalk or paint on paved surfaces (use biodegradable paint or erase residual markings as far as possible after excavation), or with wooden pegs in grassed or un-surfaced areas, preferably to one side of the service. Steel pins, spikes or long pegs which could damage services laid at shallow depth should not be used.

Safe excavation

In summary

Determine the method or technique for excavating near underground services before work starts, taking account of:

- the nature and scope of the work;
- the type, position and status of underground services;
- the ground conditions;
- site constraints.

Provide those doing the work with a written plan, including information about the location and nature of underground services. They should be competent, provided with appropriate personal protective equipment (PPE) and work equipment, and allowed sufficient time.

Identified services should be carefully exposed and clearly marked. A permit system may be appropriate for particularly hazardous work. This will involve written authorisation by a responsible person, identifying the work to be done and the precautions to be taken. A permit system needs suitable supervision and monitoring to ensure that the conditions of a permit are complied with (see paragraph 163).

Backfilling of excavations must properly support and protect the underground services. Concrete must not be used to encase services when backfilling.

If an underground service suffers damage during the excavation or subsequent work, inform the owner/operator. In the case of electricity cables, gas pipes, other pipelines or high-pressure water mains, arrange to keep people well clear of the area until it has been repaired or otherwise made safe by the owner/operator.

Exposing services

98 All those working to expose services and those supervising them must be competent to do so. They should have had sufficient information, instruction and training to:

- understand the risk to safety from damaging services;
- use detection tools;
- practise safe excavation techniques and understand the value of hand digging and the risks from using power tools or mechanical excavators.

99 Excavation work should follow safe digging practices. Once a detecting device has been used to determine position and route, excavation may proceed, with trial holes dug (using suitable hand tools or vacuum excavation), as necessary, to confirm the position of any detected services. Take special care when digging above or close to the assumed line of such a service.

100 You should carefully plan and manage mechanical excavation, which is a common source of damage to services. Another person should assist the excavator driver, from a position where they can safely see into the excavation and warn the driver of any services or other obstacles. This person should remain outside the operating radius of the excavator arm and bucket.

101 Instruct drivers to stay in the cab if a cable is struck. If drivers climb down, they may be electrocuted. When a cable is struck, the area should be isolated and secured; no one should go into the excavation or approach the excavator or the cable until the cable owner has made the damaged cable safe.

102 The danger created by damaging a gas pipe with an excavator is much greater than if the damage is done with a hand-held power tool, the opposite is true for work near electricity cables.

103 Remember that the effects may not only occur at the point of impact, for example:

■ damage to a service connection may result in unseen damage to the connection inside the building;
■ gas from a damaged pipe may travel along the line of a service pipe into a building, causing a dangerous build-up of gas there.

104 Hand-held power tools can damage services and should be used with care until the exact position of the service has been determined. You may use them to break a paved or concrete surface above a service, unless there are any indications that the service is particularly shallow or too close to the surface to be broken up.

105 Hand tools are a common source of accidents if incorrectly used. However, when used carefully, they can normally provide a satisfactory way of exposing services.

106 Make every effort to excavate alongside the service rather than directly above it. Avoid using hand-held power tools over the service unless:

■ the service has already been exposed by digging under the surface to be broken out and it is at a safe depth (at least 300 mm) below the bottom of the hard surface material; or
■ physical precautions have been taken to prevent the tool striking the service.

107 Mechanical excavators and power tools can be used to break up hard surfaces where the survey has proved that there are no services, or the services are deep enough so as not to be damaged by such tools.

108 Using hand-held power tools to break up hard surfaces often leads to accidents. Where practicable, only use such power tools 500 mm or more away from the indicated line of a service buried in or below a hard surface. Having done so, the service should then be positively located by careful hand digging under the hard surface. Gradually remove the hard surface until the cable is exposed. If the cable is not so exposed, then assume it is embedded within the surface.

109 Use a cable locator as a depth guide down the side of the excavation. The 500 mm safety margin may be reduced:

■ where congestion of services renders it impracticable; or
■ where surface obstructions limit the space available;

but **only** if the line of the cable has been positively identified by plans, confirmed by a locator, and additional precautions are used to prevent damage to the services.

110 Final exposure of the service by horizontal digging is recommended, as the force applied to hand tools can be controlled more effectively. Use insulated tools when hand digging near electric cables. In particular:

■ spades and shovels (preferably those with curved edges) should be used rather than other tools. They should not be thrown or spiked into the ground, but eased in with gentle foot pressure;
■ picks, pins or forks may be used with care to free lumps of stone etc, and to break up hard layers of chalk or sandstone;
■ picks should not be used in soft clay or other soft soils near to underground services.

Figure 7 Using an air digging tool

111 Safe methods of excavating may include vacuum excavation, which may incorporate use of water jetting and high-velocity air jets. They can be very effective in congested excavations where mechanical excavation and use of hand tools is difficult. However, they have limitations and will not work on all ground conditions or materials such as concrete.

112 Assess the precautions needed to prevent injury – to the operative or those nearby – from ejected soil and other material and put in place appropriate controls.

113 Assess carefully the use of jetting tools to excavate around cables as there is potential for old and fragile cables to be damaged by the jet of water or air.

114 **Make frequent and repeated use of locators during the course of the work. Service location is likely to become more accurate as cover is removed.**

115 **Once exposed, services may need to be supported and should never be used as handholds or footholds for climbing out of excavations.**

116 Sometimes there may be joints in cables. These may be enclosed in earthenware pipes, filled compound, or be of cast iron or plastic epoxy-filled casings. They need proper support and should not be roughly treated. Do not move, except in consultation with the owner.

117 Where gas pipes cross or run alongside excavations, changes in backfill etc may cause differential ground settlement and increased stress in the pipe. Wherever an excavation may affect support for a gas pipe, consult the owner. In some cases, it may be necessary to divert the gas pipe before work begins.

118 **Assume all services are live until disconnected and proven safe at the point of work. Obtain written confirmation of disconnection from the owner/operator before removing a redundant service.**

Protective clothing

119 Burns are the main injuries that result from damage to live electrical cables or from fire or explosion following a gas leak. In many cases, burns are made more severe by the injured person working bare-chested. Even ordinary work clothing can greatly reduce the severity of the burns and protective clothing is better. However, clothing made from man-made fibres such as nylon may melt and stick to the skin, increasing the severity of the burns.

120 Where electricity cables may be encountered during excavation work, employers should consider whether the work justifies wearing clothing designed to protect against electric arc, or flame-retardant clothing. Advice on the suitability and performance of protective clothing should be available from reputable companies specialising in its supply.

121 **Wearing protective clothing is not a substitute for a safe system of work.**

Identifying exposed services

122 Once underground services have been uncovered, failure to identify them correctly is another common cause of accidents. A wide variety of materials and colours have been used for services over the years. Furthermore, some services may be very similar in appearance and some services run in ducts made of various materials, including asbestos cement, making them difficult to identify. Adopt the following approaches until you have positively confirmed the identity of the service:

- Water pipes, electricity cables and telecommunication cables may be covered in black plastic. If any black plastic service is found, assume it is a live electricity cable.
- Iron and steel water pipes and gas pipelines may appear very similar. If any such pipe is uncovered, treat it as if it were a gas pipe.
- Always treat continuously welded steel pipes as if they contain a hazardous or high-pressure fluid.
- At collieries, beware of electricity cables, some of which are yellow or blue and may be mistaken for other services.
- On some building sites beware of electricity cables being placed in yellow service pipes or blue water pipes.
- Where there is any doubt about the identity of an exposed service treat it as an electricity cable or gas pipe until proved otherwise.

123 For modern installations, most utilities have agreed a national colour coding system for underground services, described in *Guidelines on the positioning and colour coding of underground utilities' apparatus.* This colour coding system should not be confused with the one contained in BS 1710:1984,[7] which generally applies to above-ground building and process services.

124 Remember that:

- old, non-utility services or other pipelines may not conform to this system;
- colours may look different under poor or artificial lighting;
- ducts could include any of the services.

125 Once the exposed service(s) is identified, determine its status, ie is it live or dead? **The status of the service may change, eg an electricity cable may become live or a pipe pressurised, so check the status when work near the service begins.**

Marking identified services

126 The system used to mark the identified services needs to be agreed and understood by all those working on site. If you use a colour coding system, this should correspond to the national colour coding system referred to in paragraph 123.

127 The services should be marked on site plans and on the ground. Markings on the ground are typically done with paint, though stakes, pins or posts can be used. Take great care if using stakes, pins or posts to make sure that they are not driven into ground where they could damage the services. For example, do not use them directly above the identified services.

Safety at excavations

128 Excavations should be properly supported, stepped or battered back to prevent them collapsing. Excavation support may involve the use of shuttering and shoring or a trench box system. Provide a safe means of access into the excavation, such as a secured ladder.

129 Provide edge protection, fencing and or coverings to prevent anyone falling into the excavation. Also take steps to prevent excavated material falling into the excavation.

Backfilling

130 Backfilling of any excavation should be done carefully to make sure that services are not damaged. Put back warning tiles, tape etc in their original position above the services unless visual examination after exposure showed this to be incorrect, in which case replace them above the service to which they refer. Do not use warning tape for any other purpose (for example, guarding an excavation) and do not discard it in an excavation during backfilling.

131 If road construction is close to the top of a gas pipe, ask the owner/operator about necessary precautions. Do not reduce the road construction depth without permission from the local highway or roads authority.

132 Backfill materials containing items likely to damage the services, such as large pieces of rock and hard core, should not be used. You can obtain further information on backfilling from:

■ utilities and owner/operators, for their particular services;

■ the Code of Practice (under Section 71 of the New Roads and Street Works Act 1991) *Specification for the reinstatement of openings in highways*.[8]

133 When backfilling an exposed gas pipe, observe the following:

■ Backfill material adjacent to gas plant should be suitable fine material or sand, containing no stones, bricks or lumps of concrete.
■ The backfill should be suitably compacted. Where the excavation has exposed an existing gas pipe, compaction should give comparable support and protection to that before the excavation. In all situations, compaction beneath the pipe is particularly important to prevent any settlement that would subsequently damage the pipe.
■ There should be no power compaction until 200 mm cover of selected fine fill has been suitably compacted.
■ Do not use concrete backfill within 300 mm of a gas pipe.

Use of concrete as backfill

134 Services should not be buried or encased in concrete as excavating close to them is dangerous. Using mechanical means to break up concrete can cause damage to cables or pipes which, if live, will likely mean that anyone present will be injured. Service owners should ensure that their own employees and contractors are aware that this practice is unacceptable.

Updating plans

135 If the plans or other information have proved to be inaccurate (for example, a service has been found well away from its recorded position), or if the present work changes the path or depth of a service, inform the service owners/operators (preferably before the excavation is backfilled) and they should amend their records accordingly.

136 The plans for new services should show how they have been laid, not how they were designed. Contractors may need to amend the design drawings accordingly.

Electricity cables

137 Most underground cables are laid in trenches between 450 mm and 1 m deep. Some high-voltage cables will be deeper. **However, never assume depths; you may find cables at shallower depths.**

138 In most cases, there will be no permanent surface marker posts or other visible indication of the presence of an underground cable. Even if no cables are shown on plans, or detected by a locator, there may still be cables present that could be live and you should keep a close watch for any signs that could indicate their presence.

139 A cable is positively located only when it has been safely exposed. Even then, digging should still proceed with care as there may be other cables and services adjacent or lower down. In addition, some lines of 11 kV or greater can be laid out as separate single-phase cables, spread out up to 600 mm across, particularly near cable joints. Where it is clear there is a risk of damage to a cable during the course of any work, the owner(s) may wish to be present on site.

Cables in concrete

140   It is bad practice for cables to be encased or buried in concrete. Unfortunately, it is not uncommon to find cables encased in concrete.

141   Using hand-held power tools to break up concrete can damage cables and, if the cable is live, anyone present is likely to be injured.

142 Careful planning is important to find alternative routes or, failing that, to arrange to make the cable dead. Cable owners are likely to want to attend the site to verify the circumstances surrounding any request to make dead. Electricity companies should co-operate, subject to the request being reasonable, and deal with the request as soon as possible. An alternative supply or bypass arrangement could be used to allow the cable to be made dead.

143 Work with the cable live should only be done if the circumstances mean it is unreasonable to make the cable dead, and if you take suitable precautions to prevent injury. If there is no alternative route, and the cable cannot be made dead, then you should agree alternative safe methods of excavation with the cable owners. Remember that powered hand tools used close to live cables are likely to represent the greatest risk of injury.

144 When work can proceed safely only after a cable has been made dead, the parties involved should continue to liaise to ensure that work is completed, and workers are clear, before the circuit is re-energised. A permit-to-work system may assist in managing this process.

145 Cables may have been laid directly in the ground with a bed or surround of fine soil or sand, or in cement-bound sand, or in earthenware or plastic pipes or ducts. Very occasionally, they may be in steel pipes. They may have a layer of tiles, slabs or coloured plastic marker tape laid above them. However, any such protection may have been disturbed and moved and you should not rely on them to give an accurate indication of a cable position.

Gas pipelines

146 The depth of cover for gas mains laid in a roadway is normally about 750 mm, and for those laid in a footway about 600 mm. The depth of cover for gas service connections is normally about 450 mm in both roads and footways. However, on private property, including at entry positions to buildings, the depth of cover for the service connection may be less, about 375 mm. High-pressure gas transmission pipelines are usually buried with at least 900 mm cover. **However, never assume depths; pipes may be found at shallower depths.**

147 Gas pipes are generally laid directly in the ground, although in certain soils selective backfill may have been used as a bed and pipe surround and, on occasion, pipes may be laid in ducts. Ductile iron pipe will sometimes be found wrapped in loose-fit polyethylene (PE) sleeving as protection against corrosion. PE mains may be inserted into redundant iron gas mains and PE service connection pipes may be inserted into yellow convoluted ducting on new housing estates.

148 Markers may also have been used to indicate gas services, namely:

- marker tiles, which may have been used above gas pipes; for example, when they have been laid at shallow depths in bridges or above cellars;
- coloured plastic markers, including for PE mains;
- marker posts/plates, which may show the position and size of valves or test points on gas mains.

However, such markers may have been disturbed and you should not rely on them as an accurate indicator of position.

149 Locate PE gas pipes by hand digging before mechanical excavation begins. This may also be necessary for metallic pipes if they have not been successfully located by a pipe-detecting device. This is particularly important for service connection pipes, which will not be marked on plans. A suitable hand-digging method is to dig a trial trench along the road near the kerb or in the footway where the service

connection pipes are likely to be at their shallowest. When the position and depth of the pipes have been determined, work can proceed.

150 Gas pipes may have projections such as valve housings, siphons and stand pipes that are not shown on the plans. To allow for this, do not use mechanical excavators within 500 mm of a gas pipe. The gas transporter may advise greater safety distances, depending on the pipeline pressure.

151 Never disturb pipe restraints or thrust blocks (or the ground supporting them) where they are close to gas mains as this can cause sudden failure of the main.

Gas leak or damage

152 If a gas leak is suspected, do not attempt repairs. Instead, take the following action immediately:

- Evacuate everyone from the immediate vicinity of the escape. If the service connection to a building or the adjacent main has been damaged, warn the occupants to leave the building, and any adjoining building, until it is safe for them to return.
- Inform the gas distribution network operator by telephoning the National Gas Emergency number 0800 111 999.
- Prohibit smoking, and extinguish all naked flames and other sources of ignition within at least 5 m of the leak.
- Help gas transporter staff, police or fire services, as requested.

153 Report any damage, however slight, to the owner. Where an excavation uncovers a gas pipe with a damaged wrapping, tell the owner so that they can make repairs to prevent future corrosion and leakage.

Other work near gas pipelines

154 Because of the risks they pose, do not undertake the following without consulting the pipeline owner/ operator:

- the use of explosives within 30 m of any gas pipe;
- piling or vertical boring within 15 m of any gas pipe;
- excavation work within 10 m of any above-ground gas installation;
- building a manhole, chamber or other structure over, around or under a gas pipe;
- work that results in a reduction of cover or protection over a pipe.

155 If you are to carry out welding or other hot work involving naked flames within 10 m of exposed gas plant, ask the gas transporter to check the atmosphere before work begins and continue monitoring during the

work. Take care to make sure that no damage occurs, particularly to plastic gas pipes or to the protective coatings on other gas pipes.

Water pipes and sewers

156 To avoid the effects of frost, water mains and sewers are generally laid at depths of 900 mm or more; water services to premises normally have about 750 mm cover; unless local circumstances necessitate shallower depths. In general, work near underground water pipes is of low risk and most precautions are more concerned with reducing the cost of damage than with eliminating the risk.

157 However, there are some dangers and precautions should include:

- Where work is carried out near water mains, obtain plans from the relevant water company and use a pipe locator. However, plastic pipes will not be detectable by most detecting devices. Follow safe digging practices, using hand tools as far as practicable.
- At bends in mains, concrete thrust blocks may be used. Under no circumstances should either thrust blocks or the ground supporting them be disturbed, as this can cause sudden failure of the main.
- Support exposed water pipes, as necessary, and use the correct method of backfilling. For advice, contact the relevant water company or water authority.
- If a water pipe or its wrapping is damaged, inform the relevant water company or water authority – and the owners of any other underground services which may be affected – immediately. Do not make unauthorised repairs.

Major hazard pipelines

158 These pipelines may be laid directly in the ground, although sometimes selective backfill will have been used as a bed and pipe surround. They are normally buried with at least 900 mm cover and may be even deeper where they cross roads and railways. Therefore, they are unlikely to be affected by shallow excavations.

159 Although marker posts/plates are sometimes used to indicate the position, size and ownership of pipelines, such markers may have been disturbed and you should not rely on them as an accurate indicator of position.

160 Locate pipelines by hand digging before using mechanical excavators nearby. In any event, do not use mechanical excavators within 500 mm of a pipeline.

161 Most pipelines will be protected against corrosion by a coating. This will normally be:

- coal tar or bitumen – coloured black, sometimes with traces of white limewash;
- polyethylene cladding – usually yellow;
- fusion-bonded epoxy powder – can be any colour, usually green or beige.

162 Some pipelines will be protected against corrosion by an alternative method known as cathodic protection, which will be linked to the pipeline by cabling. Both pipeline coatings and cathodic protection systems are susceptible to damage, even with hand tools, so take great care when excavating and backfilling and use a physical means of prevention (such as boards etc) where appropriate. It is important to report to the owner/operator any damage, including to the corrosion protection, before reburying the service.

Case study 4

A worker suffered severe burns after drilling in to a low-voltage cable during work to install street furniture. The electrical cable had been moved, wrapped in plastic and encased in reinforced concrete during earlier works to redevelop the street environment. Its location had not been recorded by the contractor managing the work.

The cable should not have been encased in concrete. It should have been moved in consultation with the electricity distribution company.

Permit to work

163 A permit-to-work system is a formal recorded process used to control work that is identified as potentially hazardous. It is also a means of communication between managers, supervisors and operatives who carry out the hazardous work.

164 A permit-to-work system aims to ensure that proper consideration is given to the risks of a particular job, and authorises certain people to carry out specific work at a specific site at a certain time – and sets out the precautions needed to complete the job safely.

165 Essential features of permit-to-work systems are:

- clear identification of who may authorise particular jobs and who is responsible for specifying the necessary precautions;
- clear identification of the types of work considered hazardous;
- clear identification of permitted tasks, risks, duration and control measures to be applied.

166 A permit-to-work system will be more effective if you have consulted operatives. Imposing systems without consultation can lead to procedures that do not reflect the circumstances on site.

Some specific sites and situations

Safe systems of work for trenchless methods
167 Trenchless methods are increasingly used for laying and renovating underground pipes and cables, particularly where there is a need to avoid surface disruption. The most widely used techniques are directional drilling, impact moling, microtunnelling, pipe bursting and auger boring.

168 Use plans, detecting devices and trial excavations to locate existing services in the same way as for open-cut excavation methods. The route of the device being used should then be planned accordingly to avoid colliding with, and damaging, other services. In addition, if moling or pipe bursting are undertaken too near to other services or ducts, displaced soil may damage or enter them.

169 As a general guide, to avoid damage and to allow sufficient clearance for maintenance of the services, the minimum clearance between adjacent services should be either 250 mm or one and a half times the diameter of the pipe being laid, whichever is the greater. For electricity cables, clearances for maintenance work should be approximately 300 mm.

170 However, clearances for any technique may need to be varied, taking into account such factors as the construction of adjacent plant, ground conditions, bore diameter, the accuracy and reliability of the technique/ equipment being used and whether the other plant is parallel to or crosses the proposed line. You should take into account any requirements of the owners of adjacent services.

171 Moles can be prone to deflection from their original course and, if there are existing services in the vicinity, you should use a mole-tracking device, Where you are using trenchless techniques, all equipment should be effectively earthed at all times it is in use using an equipotential mat, as required, in case it hits a power cable and causes the machinery to become live.

Figure 8 Horizontal drilling being used for laying a cable under a road

172 Further information in *Trenchless and minimum excavation techniques: Planning and selection*[9] and *Trenchless techniques*.[10]

Demolition sites
173 Special problems can arise in the case of service terminations in derelict property or on demolition sites. Anyone concerned with demolition work should give adequate notice to the relevant gas, electricity and water services of their intention to demolish any premises. Do not start work until they have confirmed in writing that either the supply has been disconnected or other appropriate safeguarding action has been taken.

174 Underground services on industrial or commercial sites may be owned by the site occupier. A contractor who is to demolish buildings or plant on such a site should contact the owner or occupier, in addition to the utilities and other service operators, to ensure that all relevant services are isolated before work starts.

175 Even where supplies have been disconnected, beware of, for example:

- services that run through sites and are not part of the site supplies;
- pot-ended or bottle-ended cables.

If in doubt, treat services as 'live'.

176 Further advice on demolition can be found in BS 6187:2011.[11]

Case study 5

A devastating explosion destroyed part of a former hospital building undergoing refurbishment to convert it into residential apartments. A demolition contractor cut through a 6-inch cast-iron gas main in an underground tunnel. No checks were made about the pipe, its contents and whether it had been properly isolated.

When doing demolition and refurbishment works, confirm that gas and electricity supplies are properly identified, located and point of isolation confirmed before work starts on site.

Appendix 1: Legislation

1   The following summary outlines the main legal requirements that apply to work near underground services. The list is not exhaustive and does not give a definitive interpretation of the law. It summarises the main issues to bear in mind when carrying out such work.

The Health and Safety at Work etc Act 1974

2   The 1974 Act applies to all work activities. Section 2(1) imposes a duty on an employer to ensure so far as is reasonably practicable the health, safety and welfare of employees while at work. This extends to the provision and maintenance of safe systems of work as well as such information, instruction, training and supervision as is necessary.

3   Section 3(1) imposes a duty on employers to take precautions, so far as is reasonably practicable, to ensure the health and safety of people not in their employment. This duty could apply to any owner/ operator of underground services, to clients, local authorities or contractors.

4   Section 3(2) imposes a similar duty on the self-employed for the health and safety of themselves and others.

5   Section 4(2) imposes a duty on people in control of non-domestic premises to ensure, so far as is reasonably practicable, the health and safety of people not in their employment who are using those premises. The definition of premises is wide-ranging and is not confined to buildings.

6   Section 7 imposes duties on each employee to take reasonable care for their own health and safety and for the health and safety of anyone else who may be affected by their acts or omissions at work, and to co-operate with their employer to enable the employer to comply with their duties.

The Management of Health and Safety at Work Regulations 1999

7   These Regulations require employers and the self-employed to assess the risks arising from work activities. They should do this with a view to identifying the measures which need to be taken to comply with relevant health and safety legislation, therefore eliminating risks where possible and controlling those which remain.

The Construction (Design and Management) Regulations 2007

8   The Construction (Design and Management) Regulations 2007 apply to all construction projects and set out requirements in relation to their design and management. They place responsibilities on all those who can contribute to improving health and safety, including clients, designers and contractors. These responsibilities relate to planning, management, design and co-operation between those involved in the project. Risks should be properly managed by action during the design, planning and execution phases of the project.

The Provision and Use of Work Equipment Regulations 1998

9   These Regulations require that equipment is maintained in good repair. Employers should ensure that employees who use work equipment or who manage or supervise its use, have received adequate training in the risks involved, methods of use and precautions to be adopted.

The Electricity at Work Regulations 1989

10   These Regulations require that those in control of part or all of an electrical system should ensure that the system is safe when provided, safe to use, and that it is maintained in a safe condition. They also require that any work activity on or near an electrical system be carried out in such a manner as to prevent danger – excavation work should not be carried out unless all suitable and sufficient steps have been taken to identify and, as far as is reasonably practicable, prevent any risk from any underground cable or other underground electrical service (regulation 4(3)).

11 Regulation 14 requires that work should not be done on or near a live conductor, where danger may arise, unless:

■ it is unreasonable in all the circumstances for it to be dead;
■ it is reasonable in all the circumstances for the work to be done while it is live;
■ suitable precautions are taken to prevent injury.

The Reporting of Injuries, Diseases and Dangerous Occurrences Regulations 2013

12 These Regulations require employers and the self-employed to report certain occupational injuries, diseases and dangerous occurrences to the relevant enforcing authority (for incidents arising during excavation work this will almost certainly be the Health and Safety Executive via an online reporting system).

13 Any work-related injury which results in a worker being unable to carry out the full range of their duties for more than seven days (including rest days and holidays) is reportable. There is also a range of injuries defined as specified injuries.

14 Where there are no reportable injuries, underground electrical cable strikes become reportable as dangerous occurrences where the resulting fire or electrical explosion had the potential to cause death, or if it puts the cable out of action for more than 24 hours.

15 Certain pipeline incidents, including gas escapes, are also reportable as dangerous occurrences by the operator of the pipeline. Schedule 2, part I, paragraphs 21 and 22 list dangerous occurrences associated with pipelines which are reportable. (Certain pipelines are exempted, corresponding to those to which the Pipelines Safety Regulations do **not** apply, eg water mains, drains and sewers.)

16 The dangerous occurrences include:

Electrical incidents causing explosion or fire

17 Any explosion or fire caused by an electrical short circuit or overload (including those resulting from accidental damage to the electrical plant) which either:

■ results in the stoppage of the plant involved for more than 24 hours; or
■ causes a significant risk of death.

18 Where the failure of an item of electrical equipment (including as a result of accidental damage) results in a fire or explosion, the failure is reportable as a dangerous occurrence if the equipment concerned is rendered unusable for over 24 hours, or if the occurrence was one with the potential to cause the death of any person. The incident is reportable even if the system in which the damaged equipment was installed is put back into service using new equipment within 24 hours. In such a case, an assessment should be made on how long a repair to the damaged equipment would have taken had it been attempted. Repair time does not include incidental time delays such as those associated with travelling to repair plant in remote locations, or with sourcing parts.

Pipelines or pipeline works

19 In relation to a pipeline or pipeline works:

■ any damage to, accidental or uncontrolled release from, or inrush of anything into a pipeline;
■ the failure of any pipeline isolation device, associated equipment or system; or
■ the failure of equipment involved with pipeline works;

which could cause personal injury to any person, or which results in the pipeline being shut down for more than 24 hours;

■ the unintentional change in position of a pipeline, or in the subsoil, which requires immediate attention to safeguard the pipeline's integrity or safety.

20 The incidents listed are reportable in respect of onshore pipelines or pipeline works. The following types of pipeline are **not** covered by these requirements:

■ a drain or sewer;
■ any pipe used to provide heating or cooling, or for domestic purposes;
■ a pipe used in the control or monitoring of plant;
■ a pipe used for the conveyance of air, water vapour or steam;
■ a water pipe, other than when used for the purposes of injecting water into an underwater well or reservoir containing mineral resources;
■ a pipeline contained wholly within the premises of a single undertaking;
■ a pipeline contained wholly within a caravan site;
■ a pipeline contained wholly within land classed as a railway asset;
■ any part of a gas-supply pipeline which is downstream of an emergency control.

21 The phrase 'accidental or uncontrolled release' is not intended to include minor leaks from pipelines, eg small leaks from valve stems, flanges etc. However, sudden or uncontrolled escapes requiring immediate attention or action should be reported.

22 Examples of reportable damage with the potential for harm would include such things as gouging, denting, buckling etc caused by external interference requiring immediate action. Such damage may or may not have resulted in any escape of the pipeline contents. External coating damage without damage to the underlying substrate would not be reportable.

The Gas Safety (Management) Regulations 1996
23 These Regulations are aimed at ensuring the natural gas distribution network is safely managed. To deal with gas leaks, they require the following:

- BG Group plc (or its successors) to provide a continuously manned, national freephone telephone service, so that people can report gas escapes;
- where BG Group plc (or its successors) is notified of escapes they should straight away notify the relevant gas conveyor or emergency service provider;
- the relevant gas conveyor or emergency service provider should go to where the gas is escaping as soon as reasonably practicable;
- gas conveyors/emergency service providers should stop gas escaping within 12 hours.

24 Where a gas escape from a service pipe or main has, or was likely to have, resulted in a fire or explosion, then the gas conveyor has to ensure an investigation is carried out.

The Pipelines Safety Regulations 1996
25 These Regulations deal with the safe design, construction and operation of pipelines. The scope includes requirements that:

- no person shall cause such damage to a pipeline as may give rise to a danger;
- pipeline operators shall take reasonable steps to inform people of the existence and whereabouts of a pipeline to prevent damage to it.

New Roads and Street Works Act 1991
26 This Act requires utilities and other undertakers (undertaker is a defined term under the Act) to give notice of their planned works under a variety of circumstances, depending upon the type of street in which the works are to be carried out and the type of works to be done. Emergency, urgent and some minor works can be started without issuing notice.

27 The Act also requires undertakers to record the location of apparatus belonging to them, to keep records up to date and to make them available for inspection at all reasonable hours, free of charge to any person having authority to carry out works in the street.

28 The terms 'emergency', 'urgent' and 'minor' works referred to above relate only to notifications for the purpose of the NRSWA and do not affect the legal obligations under the Health and Safety at Work etc Act 1974 (HSW Act) to give and obtain information needed to ensure safe working.

29 The HSW Act requirements apply to all work regardless of NRSWA classification and include work not covered by the NRSWA. There is also a specific duty on electricity companies to supply information under the Electricity Safety Quality and Continuity Regulations 2002 (see paragraph 26).

30 Section 67 of NRSWA requires that for any street works, work is supervised by a person qualified under the Street Works (Qualifications of Supervisors and Operatives) Regulations 1992. There also has to be an operative qualified under the same Regulations on site while work is in progress.

Electricity Safety Quality and Continuity Regulations 2002
31 A supplier of electricity has a duty under regulation 15 of the Regulations to make and, so far as is reasonably practicable, keep up to date 'a map or series of maps indicating the position and depth below surface level of all his works'. The supplier must provide these maps free of charge to anyone who has good reason for requiring them. Regulation 14 of the Regulations imposes requirements for the protection of underground cables and also imposes requirements for the depth and manner of their installation.

Fire Services Act 1947
32 Section 16 requires notice to be given to the fire authority of works which will affect a water supply or a fire hydrant.

References and further reading

1   *Safety at street works and road works. A Code of Practice* (also known as the Red Book) Department for Transport 2011 ISBN 978 0 1155 119580

2   *Traffic signs manual Chapter 8 (Part 1). Road works and temporary situations – design* The Stationery Office 2009 ISBN 978 0 11 553051 7

3   *Traffic signs manual Chapter 8 (Part 2). Road works and temporary situations – operations* The Stationery Office 2009 ISBN 978 0 11 553052 4

4   *Guidelines on the positioning of underground utilities apparatus for new development sites (Issue 3) Volume 2* National Joint Utilities Group 2010

5   *Guidelines on the positioning and colour coding of underground utilities' apparatus (Issue 6) Volume 1* National Joint Utilities Group 2012

6   *A guide to the Pipelines Safety Regulations 1996. Guidance on Regulations* L82 HSE Books 1996 ISBN 978 0 7176 1182 9 www.hse.gov.uk/pubns/books/l82.htm

7   BS 1710:1984 *Specification for identification of pipelines and services* British Standards Institution

8   *Specification for the reinstatement of openings in highways: A Code of Practice* (Second edition) The Stationery Office 2002 ISBN 978 0 11 552538 4

9   *Trenchless and minimum excavation techniques: Planning and selection* (SP147) Construction Industry Research and Information Association (CIRIA) ISBN 978 0 8601 7483 7

10 *Trenchless techniques* IGEM/SR/28 Institution of Gas Engineers & Managers

11 BS 6187:2011 *Code of practice for demolition* British Standards Institution

Guidance

Guidelines on the management of third party cable ducting Volume 3 National Joint Utilities Group 2007

Dealing with gas escapes IGEM/SR/29 Institution of Gas Engineers & Managers

Trenching practice (Second edition) R97 Construction Industry Research and Information Association (CIRIA) ISBN 978 0 8601 7192 8

The Reporting of Injuries, Diseases and Dangerous Occurrences Regulations (RIDDOR) www.hse.gov.uk/riddor www.hse.gov.uk/riddor/examples-reportable-incidents.htm

Memorandum of guidance on the Electricity at Work Regulations 1989. Guidance on Regulations HSR25 (Second edition) HSE Books 2007 ISBN 978 0 7176 6228 9 www.hse.gov.uk/pubns/hsr25.htm

A guide to the Gas Safety (Management) Regulations 1996. Guidance on Regulations L80 HSE Books 1996 ISBN 978 0 7176 1159 1 www.hse.gov.uk/pubns/books/l80.htm

Managing health and safety in construction. Construction (Design and Management) Regulations 2007. Approved Code of Practice L144 HSE Books 2007 ISBN 978 0 7176 6223 4 www.hse.gov.uk/pubns/books/l144.htm

Managing for health and safety www.hse.gov.uk/managing/index.htm

Useful links

HSE
www.hse.gov.uk
Source of guidance and access to HSE publications

National Joint Utilities Group
www.njug.org.uk
Source of guidance and information on street works
and detecting underground services

Energy Networks Association
www.energynetworks.org
Information about gas and electricity supply companies

Utility Strike Avoidance Group
www.utilitystrikeavoidancegroup.org
A collaborative group of utilities asset owners, industry
groups and contractors developing standards of safety
when carrying out work on services

Utility Mapping Association
www.utilitymappingassociation.com
A trade body developing standards of training and
competence for surveyors

The Survey Association
www.tsa-uk.org.uk
A trade body for commercial surveyors and source of
information about surveying companies and
technologies

Association of Geotechnical and Geoenvironmental
Specialists
www.ags.org.uk
Trade association for those involved in site
investigation. Provides guidance for clients and
practitioners

UKOPA
www.ukopa.co.uk
Industry body for pipeline operators. Source of
information about pipeline safety

UKSTT
ukstt.org.uk
Source of information about trenchless technology

Linewatch
www.linewatch.co.uk/index.php
Source of information and guidance about some major
hazard pipelines

British Standards Institution
www.bsigroup.co.uk

Institution of Gas Engineers & Managers
www.igem.org.uk

Electrical Safety Council
www.electricalsafetycouncil.org.uk

Further information

For information about health and safety visit
https://books.hse.gov.uk or http://www.hse.gov.uk.
You can view HSE guidance online and order priced
publications from the website. HSE priced publications
are also available from bookshops.

To report inconsistencies or inaccuracies in this guidance
email: commissioning@williamslea.com.

British Standards can be obtained in PDF or hard copy formats
from BSI: http://shop.bsigroup.com or by contacting
BSI Customer Services for hard copies only Tel: 0846 086 9001
email: cservices@bsigroup.com.

The Stationery Office publications are available from
The Stationery Office, PO Box 29, Norwich NR3 1GN
Tel: 0333 202 5070 Fax: 0333 202 5080.
E-mail: customer.services@tso.co.uk Website: www.tso.co.uk.
They are also available from bookshops.

Statutory Instruments can be viewed free of charge at
www.legislation.gov.uk where you can also search for
changes to legislation.